FORCES OF
NATURE

By the Editors of Creative

Creative Educational Society, Inc.
Mankato, Minnesota

Published simultaneously in Canada by J. M. Dent & Sons, Ltd., Don Mills, Ontario

Standard Book Number: 87191-075-6

Library of Congress Catalog Card Number: 73-140636

Printed in the United States.

CONTENTS

INTRODUCTION

Nothing in man's natural environment has such a continuous impact on his life as the changing aspects of the atmosphere which we call weather. The farmer's work, the construction of new buildings, the number of shoppers in a store, the plans for a picnic, all depend on the weather of the day. A hurricane striking the Atlantic coast without warning may do great damage to houses and ships and even bring about the loss of human life. A snowstorm will tie up traffic and leave many motorists stranded, and towns and villages isolated. A prolonged rainfall may lead to washouts, landslides, and disastrous floods. An ice storm may bring down power and telephone lines, cutting off the supply of electricity and interrupting communications for thousands of families.

Man cannot prevent these disasters. But he has learned much about the workings of the atmosphere and about the causes of the different types of weather and climate. This knowledge, although still far from perfect, has made it possible to forecast what to expect so that preparations can be made to guard against these violent outbursts of the atmosphere and to plan ahead of time according to the anticipated weather.

The purpose of this book is to give a brief introduction in non-technical language what the atmosphere is made of, and what kinds of weather and climate are found at different seasons and in different parts of the world.

If you study the text and pictures carefully, you will be able to observe many examples of the different kinds of weather phenomena which are discussed in this book.

You will then become familiar with the fascinating, ever-changing moods of our atmosphere which affect all human activities and all life on the earth.

Internal unrest

This aerial view of one of the world's largest craters (one mile across) shows the size and activity of the Poas Volcano in Costa Rica. Tremendous internal forces develop this violent activity, which we name volcanism. This force comes out as the escape of excessive heat.

With increasing depth, earth temperatures increase. Measurements indicate that rock temperatures increase at about 1° C. per 100 feet of descent. Fortunately, this increase is not maintained to the center of the earth. It is estimated that at 60 miles down, temperatures have increased to probably abound 1500° C. This is hot enough to melt rock at the earth's surface. Scientists agree, however, that rocks at this depth are normally unable to melt because of enormous pressures upon them.

Conditions to form melted rock (magma) below volcanoes may depend upon extra heat from deeper levels within the earth. Wherever the rock does melt, the very hot magma, or liquid rock, may force its way up to the surface through the earth's crust. When the magma reaches the earth's surface, it is erupted out onto the surface in the form of lava, volcanic dust, volcanic cinders, or volcanic ash. These forms of volcanic debris pile up to change the surface of the earth.

Birth of a volcano

How does a volcano begin? This question can be answered by studying the photograph and examining the story of this recent volcanic eruption.

The Paricutin volcano had its beginning when the area became disturbed by slight earthquakes in February, 1943. These tremors continued until cracks appeared in a level cornfield on February 20. The beginning of the volcano was observed by a farmer and his wife as a column of ash and dust began to rise from the cornfield. The village was alerted, and they watched as the column grew. The next day the column had a large cloud of smoke pouring out the mouth of a cinder cone 100 feet high. The cone was built up by rock, cinders, ash, and lava flows to a height of 500 feet in two weeks; 1,100 feet in three months; and 1,400 feet in the first year. Rocks and dust were thrown out as explosions occurred every few seconds.

Scientists arrived and began to record, measure, and photograph the birth of this volcano. The cone soon cracked, and lava began to flow. Some of the flows spread out six miles. All the fields and woods for miles around the volcano were destroyed by lava, ash, and cinders. Several villages were covered and destroyed.

The photograph shows the lava flow in the foreground, ash-plumed Paricutin in the background and other cinder cones similar to the Paricutin. These volcanoes show little erosion and must be post-glacial in age. The Paricutin is only unique in that it was the last volcano to come into existence in this area.

An active volcano

The Hawaiian Islands are entirely volcanic but the island of Hawaii is the only one with active volcanoes. Kilauea is one of five major volcanic centers on this island. Kilauea is no longer an independent mountain, having been partly buried by the immense Mauna Loa volcano that rises 30,000 feet from the ocean floor. Kilauea Iki, "Iki" meaning small, is located inside the larger crater of Kilauea, and is a small center of eruptive activity. In this picture it is not possible to see all of Kilauea, but it is a large shield dome that rises some 20,000 feet from the floor of the Pacific Ocean.

Kilauea Iki renewed its activity in 1959, when this photograph was taken. Its action is typical of volcanoes on the Hawaiian Islands. Action is called the mild eruptive or oozing type. When Kilauea Iki erupted, there were no violent outbursts or explosions.

There were only the fountain-like displays of glowing gas and fiery lava fragments pictured in this photograph. These brilliant fire fountains are nearly 1,000 feet high. A deep molten pool glows in the center of the crater. You can see molten lava winding its way in liquid-rock streams down onto the floor of the big crater, Kilauea. This red stream of lava has great destructive capacity to the land and often to the people. In areas where the volcanic action is violent, gases and ash are as destructive as lava. After many years, lava beds and ash deposits become soil and provide fertile land for man.

The shield shape of the quiet or oozing volcano is formed by the slowly moving, then solidifying, lava emitted by the volcano. The gentle slopes of the shield volcano are not over 10°, and their summits are usually topped by a wide, shallow depression.

10

11

Development of a caldera

Crater Lake, located in southern Oregon, is one of the outstanding scenic wonders of the United States. Its beauty is not only in its structure, but in its setting on the crest of the volcanic Cascade Range.

The lake itself is almost circular, with an unusually large diameter of nearly six miles and a depth of 2,000 feet. It is encircled by steep cliffs 500 to 2,000 feet high. The waters of the lake, as you can see, are deep blue, broken only by a 780-foot cinder cone known as Wizard Island.

The original volcano of Crater Lake, named Mt. Mazama, is one of many large volcanic mountains in the Cascades. From glacial debris found embedded with the volcanic lava, cinders, and ash, geologists have established that Mt. Mazama was active during and following the Ice Age.

Crater Lake, pictured here, is a prime example of one of nature's most spectacular phenomena, the formation of a caldera, an oversize crater. The caldera on Mt. Mazama could have been formed by violent explosions which blew off the top of the volcano, or by the collapse of the top of the volcano into the lava chamber below the volcano. Some geologists believe that in the case of Mt. Mazama, there was an engulfment. If the top had been blown off by an explosion, the slopes of the volcano would be covered with a vast amount of debris from the top of the cone. Not finding this debris, it is believed that the cone collapsed due to loss of support in the lava chamber.

13

Glaciers transform continents

Parts of North America looked like this in the great Ice Age. Glaciers covered continents during the great Ice Age. A large ice cap, pictured here, still covers more than five million square miles on the continent of Antarctica. This is an area nearly twice the size of the United States.

The conditions that cause ice to accumulate and then move down mountain valleys are similar to those which cause the formation of great continental ice sheets. Ice accumulated over three major centers in North America during the last Ice Age. One center grew on Greenland and still

remains. Another developed in the Hudson Bay-Labrador region, and a third built up ice on the Canadian Rocky Mountains. Ice moved outward from these centers like batter on a waffle iron. Tongues of ice moved outward in the lowest areas. The tongues flowed together to form massive sheets and then spread again until the central mound of accumulating snow and ice could no longer feed the ever-growing sheet. Ice covered the lands of the northern hemisphere with a "skull" cap many thousands of feet thick. The cap slid down over the United States until most of the northern states were under its frosty weight.

15

Formation of glacial ice

Snow in the high mountains or the polar regions, which fails to melt completely during the following summers, may accumulate to great depths in mountain valleys. Snow piling up layer upon layer gradually changes to a loose, granular ice, then to compacted ice and then to a firm ice mass. When the solid ice mass accumulates to a depth of one hundred feet or more, the ice molds together like soft plastic. Under the great weight of the overlying ice, the lower portions may then start to flow; and at this moment the ice mass becomes a glacier, and the ice is called glacial ice. If the compacted ice never has the opportunity to flow or move, it is then called an ice field, or if it is snow — a permanent snowfield.

Ice in motion behaves like a very thick liquid, flowing downhill along drainage channels or valleys. In the high mountains, glaciers pour out of their collecting areas and down the valleys. The moving ice eventually reaches a point in the valley where the average annual temperature is high enough to melt each year's accumulation of snow, and the glacial ice becomes exposed at the surface. The ice melts a little each summer, resulting in a net loss of the ice mass.

In this photograph, the collecting area of one glacier is marked by the smooth, flat white area in the upper right corner. This glacier flows downward toward the center of the bottom edge of the picture and probably passes the ice line at the narrow point in the valley where the ice appears to be brown and dirty. The right glacier joins another flowing in from the left in the lower center of the photograph. The large mountain is splattered with snowfields on the very steep slopes.

Glaciers make icebergs

Some glaciers reach the sea before they stop. We know that ice floats. If the ice is hundreds of feet thick, several hundred feet (about 90 percent) is submerged.

Glaciers moving into a body of water may break up there, or they may push outward until the bouyancy of the water begins to support the ice front. The crevassed and wasting ice then breaks away from the main body of the glacier to form icebergs — blocks of glacial ice. Icebergs may be small, like the ones in this picture, or they may be enormous, such as the one which sank the great ocean liner Titanic in 1912 with fifteen hundred people on board. That iceberg is thought to have weighed 200,000 tons or more.

Glaciers reaching the sea from the ice cap of Greenland are estimated to deposit as much as 25 cubic miles of ice into the North Atlantic Ocean in a single year. Rink Glacier, on the west coast of Greenland, is estimated to cast 500,000,000 tons of ice into the sea about every two weeks. In this picture, the icebergs rise only a few feet above the water. The very large ones from Greenland and Antarctic glaciers may be a mile or more long and rise 300 feet above the surface of the ocean.

Erosion by water

In 1851, Samuel St. John, geologist, spoke of erosion as follows: "The sculpture and degradation of the lands are performed partly by shore waves, partly by glaciers, partly by the wind; but chiefly by rain and running water."

This picture of the Falls of the Little Colorado River shows many characteristics of desert rivers and young streams. The river has developed a waterfall which it perpetuates by eroding out the softer beds beneath the hard sandstone in each step of the falls.

The hard beds will break off in chunks from time to time, causing the falls to slowly retreat upstream. One such chunk can be seen near the bottom of the picture. The river is carrying a large load of mud in suspension, judging by the color. At some time in the recent geologic past, a lava flow has entered the canyon of this river, and now forms the left side of the canyon in this picture. In addition to carrying off the material brought in by its tributaries, this river is eroding and deepening its channel.

21

Erosion by wind

The picking up of sand and dust by the wind is called "defiation." The ability of the wind to carry particles increases sharply as the velocity of the wind increases; a gentle breeze can carry sand grains up to 1 mm. in diameter. Since winds are common in the desert, and the bare ground is widely exposed, dust storms and sand storms are common. Certain areas of deserts have been so swept by winds that the surface is covered with a pavement of wind-polished rock cobbles.

Since a wind can carry sand grains, it is not surprising that the sand-laden wind can act as a natural sand blast. A few minutes of brisk wind in an area of loose sand can pit a glass windshield so badly that it must be replaced. The abrasive action against an outcropping rock face will in time pick out the softer portions of the rock leaving it pock-marked with holes. This photograph is an excellent example of wind-eroded sandstone south of Hayden, Colorado. Cementing silica is concentrated in innumerable little veins. Therefore, the wind could pick out the less-cemented parts of the rock, grain by grain. The young girl is looking at all the little holes the wind has made. The remaining network of sandstone indicates where this structure has enough silica to cement the grains together.

Mechanical weathering

As soon as rocks are taken out of the environment in which they were formed, and exposed to the atmosphere, mechanical and chemical forces go to work to reduce them to finer and finer particles, until they ultimately become dust. This is weathering. Often all of these forces are acting on the rocks at the same time, although the degree of their importance will vary from climate to climate.

Mechanical forces of weathering include expansion and contraction, due to heating and cooling; freezing and thawing; and to some degree, the force exerted by plants and their roots.

The rock in the photograph is a coarse granite which has been deeply weathered over thousands of years. It has recently been exposed in the road cut. The weathering has proceeded long enough to allow the whole rock to become so "rotten" that a chunk can scarcely be picked up without crumbling into individual grains. The feldspars and micas are partially altered to softer, weaker minerals, and this coarse gravel of quartz and feldspar, mixed with clay and chlorite, is visible in the photograph trailing down from the outcrop toward the foreground of the picture in a miniature talus slope. The gravel will be carried away by active erosion.

John Rathbone
Monkmeyer

25

A tornado

The tornado is known by several different names: tornado, twister, cyclone, whirlwind. It also is confused with a hurricane. A tornado is a rapidly rotating funnel-shaped cloud, resembling an elephant's trunk, which grows from the base of a thunderstorm cloud downward to the ground. The funnel averages 500 to 1,000 feet in diameter.

In the United States an average of about 600 tornadoes occur each year. Tornadoes occur at all hours of the day and night but are most frequent between 3 and 7 p.m. They also occur during every month of the year with most taking place in the spring and early summer. This time of year is most favorable because both very cold air and warm, humid air are prevalent. The advancing cold air acts as a wedge which forces the humid air to rise. The heat released when the water vapor in the rising air condenses into clouds provides the intense energy that is needed by a thunderstorm to produce tornadoes.

Thunderstorms from which tornadoes descend rotate in a counterclockwise direction. Since tornadoes are part of the larger thunderstorm cloud, they rotate in the same direction as the parent cloud. Sometimes only one tornado is associated with a rotating thunderstorm, but thunderstorms are capable of producing groups of from two to half a dozen or more during the duration of the thunderstorm.

As a funnel-shaped tornado descends from the base of the cloud, the winds that are flowing into the rapidly rotating funnel can stir up dirt near the ground before the funnel reaches the surface.

When the funnel is fully in contact with the ground, it becomes much broader with everything and everyone at the mercy of its 500-m.p.h. winds. People and automobiles are tossed about like pieces of paper, blades of grass are driven into trees, buildings explode due to the very low pressure within the funnel. The photograph shows what happens when a tornado passes over a plowed field. The loose dirt is caught in the rotating winds around the funnel, and some of it is being thrown out of the top of the debris column, especially noticeable on the right. It can be noted that the base of the cloud near the funnel is also caught in the more rapid rotation of the tornado.

J. Dalen Shellhammer

Earthquakes

Scientists generally agree that an earthquake occurs after a large mass of rock under the earth's surface breaks. After the break, the rock rebounds, or snaps back. Vast amounts of energy are released during the rebound. This energy is changed into vibrations that literally cause the earth around the break to quake.

Earthquakes occur most frequently in areas where there is a fault, or break, in the earth's crust. Faults are created when a large rock mass beneath the earth's surface begins to crack in two, and the mass on one side moves in relation to the mass on the other side. This movement may be up or down, or to the left or right.

In a large fault, movement does not occur all at once, but from time to time over perhaps thousands of years. What causes earthquakes is the sudden cracking — once every 20 or 100 or 500 years — in part of the rock mass along the fault.

During the powerful Alaskan earthquake of March 27, 1964 the earth shook violently. Only 10 percent of Alaska's land area was affected, but damage was great because half the people in the state live in this area.

Stewart
Free Lance Photographers Guild, Inc.

Rain

A season's span of weather reveals that rainfall can differ from one storm to the next. Sometimes the rain falls in a continuous drizzle all day. At other times it is in the form of showers which dump a great deal of water in a few minutes and then stop. The way in which the rain forms is similar in both cases, but the type of cloud from which it falls is different.

Clouds are made visible by the millions of tiny cloud droplets of which they are composed. The cloud droplets are actually very small spheres of water.

The convective clouds shown in this picture develop from a localized area of rising air. Since air cools as it rises, the water vapor eventually condenses into cloud droplets. The heat that is given off during the condensation process causes the air rising through the cloud to be accelerated upward. The rising air in the cloud continues to cool, therefore more of the water vapor condenses with height. As the cloud grows, the cloud droplets bump into each other and form into larger droplets. After this process continues for a while, the drops become large enough to start falling down through the rising air, increasing in size on the way down. Once the downdraft replaces the rising air that feeds moisture into the cloud, the cloud no longer continues to grow. When the downrush of drops reaches the ground, a sudden shower begins and it continues until all of the larger droplets in the cloud have fallen out. Such a shower of rain can be seen in the picture.

William Belknap
Rapho Guillumette

How a rainbow is formed

As its name suggests, a rainbow is a bow that is associated with rain, but it also can be associated with mist. Those who have seen rainbows know that they form in the direction opposite to that of the sun. Usually this occurs in the afternoon as a rain-shower moves away, leaving the sun shining on the rain.

The light that is seen by the eye results from sunlight entering raindrops and being reflected before it leaves the droplet. One reflection produces the brighter, primary bow and two reflections lead to the fainter, secondary bow. A raindrop acts like a prism when light passes through it. The colorless light from the sun is broken up into the component colors of a rainbow — red, orange, yellow, green, blue, indigo, violet.

Red light is bent the most when it passes through either a prism or raindrop. Red, therefore, should be on the outside of the primary bow and on the inside of the secondary bow, as shown in the rainbow pictured.

All of the colors of the rainbow listed above are not visible in the picture. It also should be noted that the colors reddish orange, yellow, and green do not have sharp boundaries but blend into one another. The actual colors that are visible in a rainbow depend on the size of the water drops. Large raindrops produce very bright reds, greens, and violets. Very small droplets, of the size found in fog, lead to colorless, white fogbows.

Bob Beckman
Shostal

33

Fog

Fog is a familiar weather phenomena, one which is commonly seen on a clear night with very light winds. The distance that one can see through the fog varies greatly with weather conditions. Sometimes fog is so thick that objects twenty feet away are obscured. In other cases it can be so light that one is not immediately aware that it is present; this is the situation shown in the picture. The flaming red tree in the foreground is so clear that one would have no inkling that the tree is in the fog.

However, as one looks at the trees that are farther and farther away, they become hazier and hazier as they disappear into the fog. This effect is due to the fact that the individual fog droplets are so small and so far apart that they do not obscure the nearer objects. However, when looking at a distant object, there is an increasing number of droplets between the viewer and the object, resulting in the object's becoming dimmer with distance.

Esther Henderson
Rapho Guillemette

Dew and frost

Dew and frost result from water vapor in the air coming into contact with an object that is considerably cooler than the air. In the out-of-doors, dew or frost forms on grass, ground, and other low objects. The water droplets that form indoors on a "steamed-up" window are equivalent to dew. The etchings on the inside of a window during the winter are the indoor version of frost on the ground or on objects near the ground, following a subfreezing night.

During the night, the surface of the earth becomes quite cool as it radiates the heat that it has gained during the day. Eventually the ground, grass, bushes, etc., become colder than the temperature of the air. Then the excess vapor condenses into droplets as soon as the air comes in contact with the colder objects.

Frost forms in precisely the same way that dew does, except that the temperature at which the air becomes saturated is below the freezing temperature of water. So instead of droplets forming, an intricate pattern of ice crystals appears. The successive ice crystals that form become interlocked so that they result in feathery or bristly appearing frost. When frost forms on a window that is below freezing, it grows into an overlapping feather-like design.

Books in the OUR CHANGING ENVIRONMENT Series

FORCES OF NATURE
HISTORY OF THE EARTH
LIFE IN THE SEA
GEOLOGY OF THE EARTH
OUR NATURAL ENVIRONMENT
ECOLOGY OF NORTH AMERICA

For more information about these and other quality books
for young people, please write.

CREATIVE EDUCATIONAL SOCIETY, INC.
515 North Front Street/Mankato, Minnesota 56001